TO YOSEF COHEN

WITH BLESSINGS

יְבָרֶכְךָ אֲדֹנָי וְיִשְׁמְרֶךָ

יָאֵר אֲדֹנָי פָּנָיו אֵלֶיךָ וִיחֻנֶּךָּ

יִשָּׂא אֲדֹנָי פָּנָיו אֵלֶיךָ וְיָשֵׂם לְךָ שָׁלוֹם

AND LOVE

LEVI AND FEIGE SUDAK

12 CHESHVAN 5776

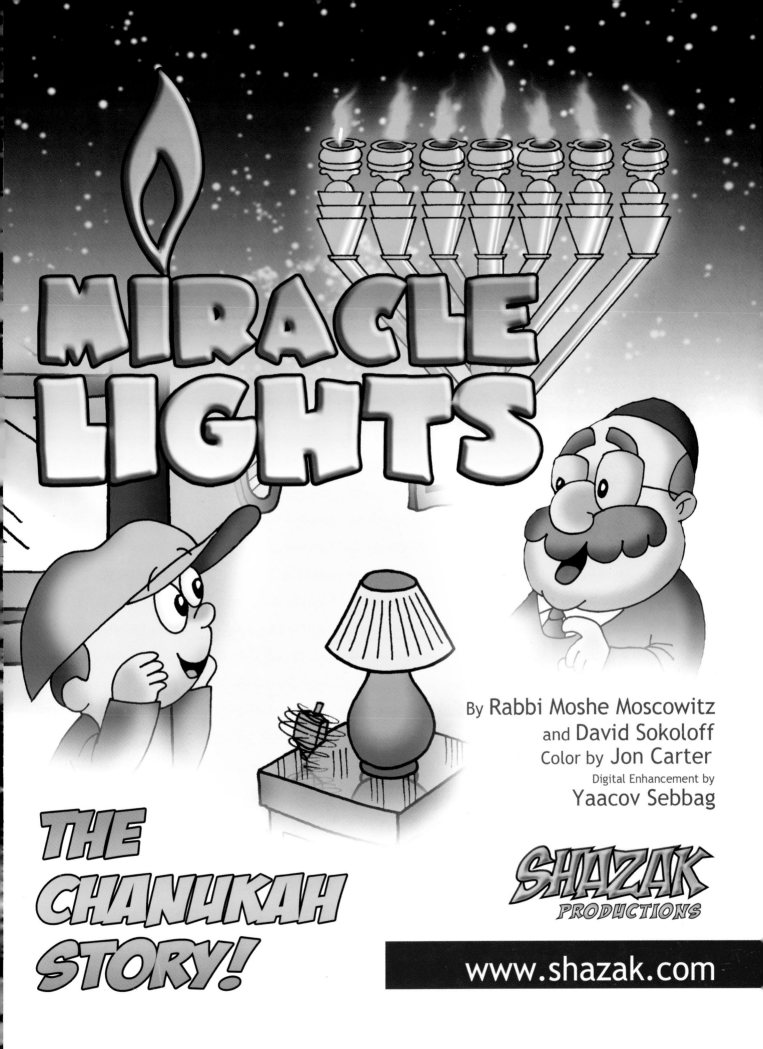

Get the marvelous MIRACLE LIGHTS animated cartoon!
Go to www.shazak.com

ISBN 1-930925-06-9

Distributed by:

FELDHEIM PUBLISHERS
200 Airport Executive Park
Nanuet, NY 10954
www.feldheim.com

Printed in China

TABLE OF CONTENTS

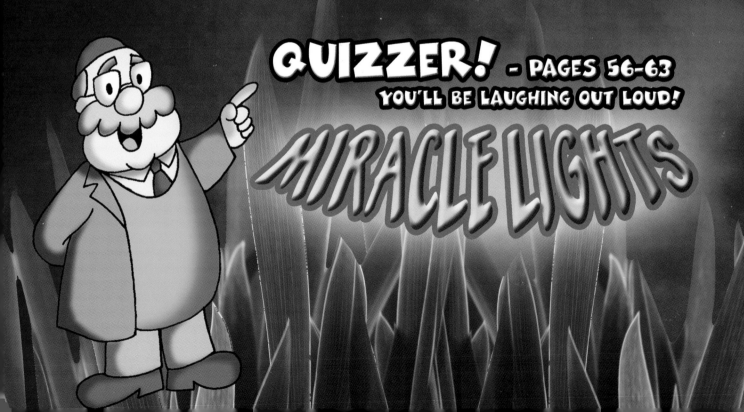

MIRACLE LIGHTS

בס"ד

Miracle Lights is dedicated to my dear wife Leah.
Not a word would have been written without
your love, support and guidance.

Special thanks to the super Shazak staff for bringing to life
the first three Shazak Productions:
Miracle Lights (Chanukah) - Book & DVD
Queen of Persia (Purim) - Book & DVD
Out of Egypt (Passover) - Book & DVD

David Sokoloff - Writer & Illustrator
John Napiorkowski - Animator
Jon Carter - Color Compositing
Yaacov Sebbag - Digital Enhancement
Michael Shoshani - Recording Engineer
Leah Moscowitz - Consultant

You have all used your amazing creative talents
to brighten the lives of countless people - young and old!

Rabbi Moshe Moscowitz
Executive Producer
Shazak Productions

THERE YOU ARE! WHAT TOOK YOU SO LONG?

ZIP!

JOSH INVITED ME TO GO WITH HIM TO THE BIG WRESTLING MATCH TONIGHT! CAN I PLEASE GO, HUH? *PLEASE...*
PALEEEEEEZE!

BENNY, YOU KNOW THAT CHANUKAH IS FAMILY TIME. WHEN WE LIGHT THE MENORAH, WE ALWAYS DO IT TOGETHER.

AND CHANUKAH IS ONE OF THE HOLIDAYS THAT HAS KEPT THE JEWISH PEOPLE TOGETHER THROUGHOUT THE CENTURIES... WE'VE BEEN CELEBRATING IT FOR OVER 2,000 YEARS.

I WOULD'VE GOTTEN BORED AFTER THE FIRST 500 YEARS.

7

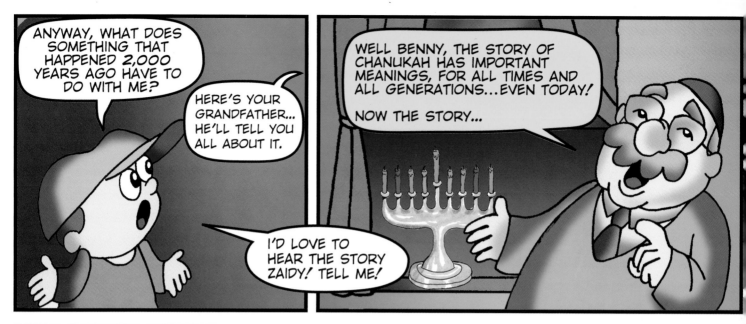

ANYWAY, WHAT DOES SOMETHING THAT HAPPENED 2,000 YEARS AGO HAVE TO DO WITH ME?

HERE'S YOUR GRANDFATHER... HE'LL TELL YOU ALL ABOUT IT.

I'D LOVE TO HEAR THE STORY ZAIDY! TELL ME!

WELL BENNY, THE STORY OF CHANUKAH HAS IMPORTANT MEANINGS, FOR ALL TIMES AND ALL GENERATIONS...EVEN TODAY!

NOW THE STORY...

LONG, LONG AGO, THE JEWS OF ANCIENT ISRAEL WERE RULED BY THE KING OF THE NEIGHBORING COUNTRY...SYRIA.

FOR A WHILE, THE JEWS WERE LEFT IN PEACE, TO FARM...

TO RAISE SHEEP AND CATTLE...

MOO

BAAA

TO BUY AND SELL IN THE MARKETPLACE...

MOSHE! THOSE CANDLES WERE SUPPOSED TO BE DELIVERED LAST WEEK!

8

TO LEARN TORAH AND DO MITZVOT (GOOD DEEDS).

THIS IS FOR YOU.

ALEPH, BET, GIMMEL, DALET!

IN THEIR GREAT CITY OF JERUSALEM, THEY HAD BUILT A MAGNIFICENT TEMPLE, THE BEIT HAMIKDASH. THERE THEY COULD WORSHIP GOD AND CELEBRATE THEIR SPECIAL FESTIVALS. AND SO THE JEWS LIVED IN PEACE AND CONTENTMENT.

BUT IT WAS NOT TO LAST...

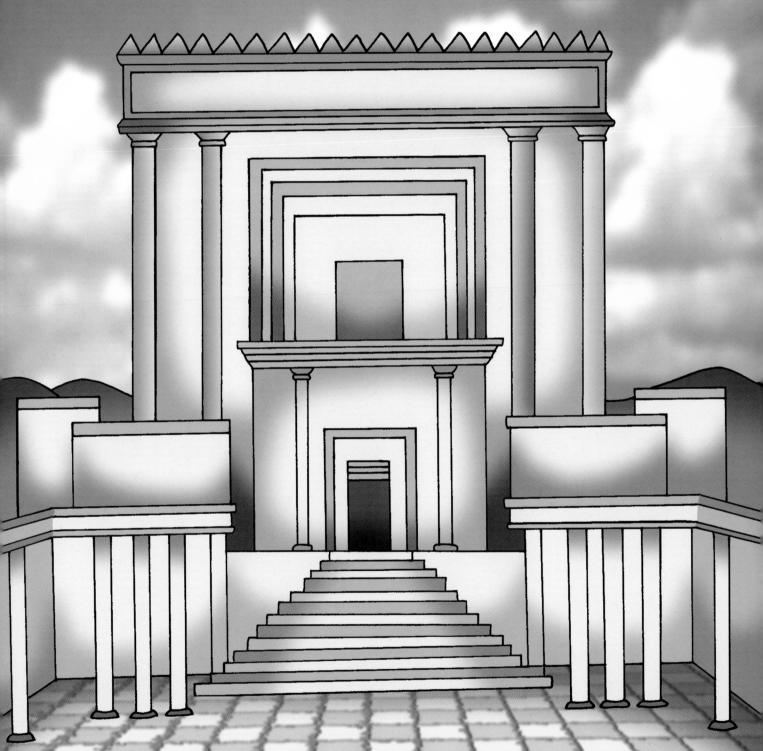

HOW WERE THE GREEKS DIFFERENT FROM THE JEWS, ZAIDY?

OH, IN THE MOST IMPORTANT WAYS!

TO THE GREEKS, THE MAIN THING IN LIFE WAS TO HAVE PLEASURE. THAT WAS THEIR WHOLE WAY OF LOOKING AT THINGS.

HICCUP

GOBBLE

GLUG GLUG GLUG

DOESN'T JUDAISM BELIEVE IN PLEASURE AND ENJOYING LIFE TOO?

OF COURSE BENNY. BUT THE TORAH TELLS US THAT THE WAY TO ACHIEVE TRUE HAPPINESS IS BY HELPING OTHERS; FILLING THE WORLD WITH DEEDS OF GOODNESS AND KINDNESS.

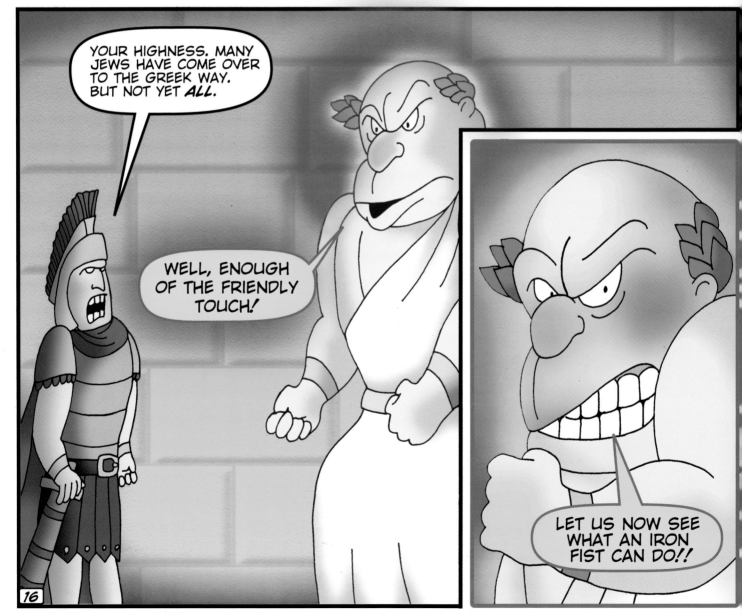

THOSE AWFUL GREEKS! WHAT'S SO GREAT ABOUT BEING BIG AND STRONG AND FULL OF CULTURE 'N STUFF, IF YOU JUST BECOME A CREEP?!

THAT'S RIGHT, BENNY. JUDAISM TEACHES THAT THE WORLD IS NOT SUPPOSED TO BE A JUNGLE, WHERE THE STRONG HUNT THE WEAK.

OR A BEAUTY SALON WHERE OUTER APPEARANCES ARE WORSHIPPED.

OR A WRESTLING MATCH WHERE PEOPLE CHEER AT OTHERS GETTING BEATEN UP!

SO... WHAT IT IS THE WORLD SUPPOSED TO BE LIKE?

OUR RABBIS SAY THAT THE WORLD IS LIKE ONE BIG FAMILY.... A FAMILY THAT ALWAYS INCREASES IN ACTS OF GOODNESS AND KINDNESS. THIS IS HOW WE BRING LIGHT TO THE WORLD!

I GET IT! THAT'S WHY WE LIGHT ANOTHER CANDLE ON EACH NIGHT OF CHANUKAH!

19

SOON THE SOUND OF MARCHING TROOPS COULD BE HEARD ON THE STEPS OF THE THE HOLY TEMPLE!

IN THE ULTIMATE OUTRAGE, THE SOLDIERS OF ANTIOCHUS DARED TO BRING IDOL-WORSHIP INTO THE BEIT HAMIKDASH ITSELF!

HURRY UP, MEN! GET THOSE STATUES IN THERE! AND DON'T WORRY ABOUT WIPING THE MUD OFF YOUR BOOTS.

AS THE HEARTBROKEN JEWS LOOKED ON...

HEY, LUCIUS RIDICULUS, WHERE DO YOU WANT US TO SACRIFICE THIS PIG?

UH, RIGHT HERE BY THE ZEUS IDOL.

HAR HAR HAR HAR HAR HAR

AND THESE GUYS CALL ME A PIG!

23

NOT LONG AFTERWARD, THE GREEKS CAME TO MODI'IN, AND SET UP A HUGE IDOL IN THE MIDDLE OF THE VILLAGE.

ME! ME! I'LL DO IT!

WHO WANTS TO SACRIFICE TO THE GREAT ZEUS? YOU WILL BE HANDSOMELY REWARDED!

BUT MATTITYAHU DID NOT STAND IDELY BY...

MY FELLOW JEW SHOULD WORSHIP A SENSELESS BLOCK OF STONE?!

NEVER!!!

IN HIS HIDEAWAY IN THE HILLS OF JUDEA, THE COURAGEOUS MATTITYAHU SUMMONS HIS FIVE BRAVE SONS.

SPREAD THE WORD THROUGH-OUT THE LAND. FIGHT THE GREEKS AND GET RID OF THEM ONCE AND FOR ALL!

BUT FATHER, HOW CAN WE BEAT THE THOUSANDS OF TRAINED SOLDIERS OF ANTIOCHUS?

REMEMBER, THE LAND OF ISRAEL IS A LAND OF HOLINESS. THE GREEKS HAVE BROUGHT IDOLATRY, MURDER AND CRUELTY TO IT.

AND GOD WILL HELP US CLEANSE THE LAND OF THEM!

NO MATTER HOW LONG THE FIGHT, NO MATTER WHAT THE COST, WE SHALL WIN!

WHOEVER IS ON THE SIDE OF GOD, LET THEM JOIN US!

AND SO, JEWS BEGAN TO JOIN MATTITYAHU AND HIS SONS. THEY CAME FROM FARMS, SHOPS, AND SCHOOLS. FROM TOWNS, CITIES, AND VILLAGES ALL OVER THE LAND, THEY CAME TO THE HILLS TO DO THEIR PART TO FREE ISRAEL FROM THE GRIP OF ANTIOCHUS. BUT IT WAS NOT GOING TO BE EASY.

A GOOD NUMBER OF BRAVE MEN JOINED THE REVOLT, BUT NONE OF THEM EXACTLY PROFESSIONAL SOLDIERS, IF YOU KNOW WHAT I MEAN...

BINYAMIN! HOLD THAT SPEAR STRAIGHT! YOU LOOK LIKE A FARMER.

WHAT DO YOU WANT FROM ME? I AM A FARMER.

OOOF!

HEY! WATCH WHERE YOU'RE WAVING THAT SWORD, WILL YA?!

ALL RIGHT MEN, LINE UP AND FALL IN... NO, NOT FALL DOWN, FALL IN!

I CAN'T SEE WITH THIS HELMET ON.

YOU GOT IT ON BACKWARDS!

OUCH, MOSHE. YOU STEPPED ON MY TOE.

HOW'S THE TRAINING GOING, ELAZAR?

WELL, THE MEN ARE CERTAINLY DEDICATED TO WINNING THIS WAR, YEHUDAH, BUT AS THINGS STAND NOW, THEY FIGHT LIKE SHEPHERDS.

28

THAT'S ALL RIGHT... WHEN THEIR FLOCK IS IN DANGER, SHEPHERDS CAN FIGHT LIKE WOLVES!

AND DON'T FORGET ELAZAR, WE KNOW OUR LAND AND THE GREEKS DON'T. WE KNOW THE BEST PLACES TO LEAD THE ENEMY INTO AN AMBUSH...

WE'LL ATTACK THEM BY SURPRISE OVER AND OVER UNTIL THEY ARE **TOTALLY DEFEATED!**

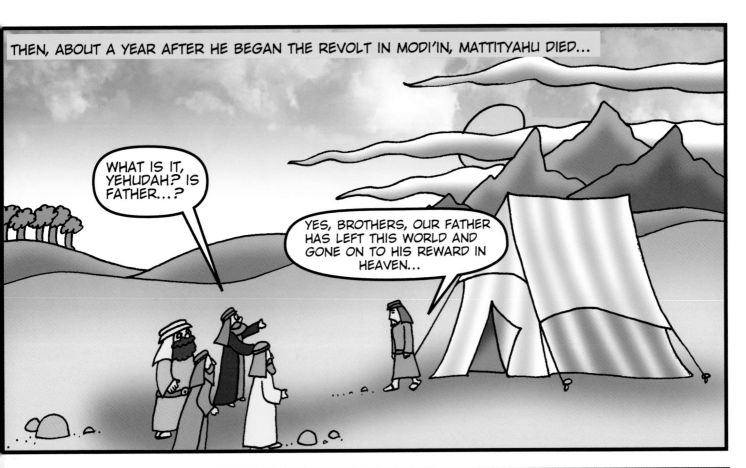

THEN, ABOUT A YEAR AFTER HE BEGAN THE REVOLT IN MODI'IN, MATTITYAHU DIED...

WHAT IS IT, YEHUDAH? IS FATHER...?

YES, BROTHERS, OUR FATHER HAS LEFT THIS WORLD AND GONE ON TO HIS REWARD IN HEAVEN...

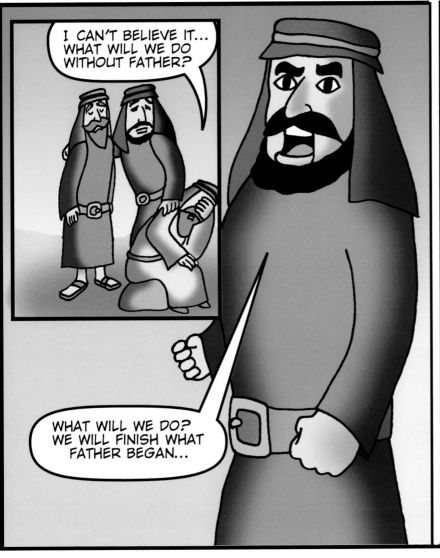

I CAN'T BELIEVE IT... WHAT WILL WE DO WITHOUT FATHER?

WHAT WILL WE DO? WE WILL FINISH WHAT FATHER BEGAN...

WE SHALL DRIVE THE GREEKS, THEIR SWORDS, IDOLS, AND ALL... *OUT OF ISRAEL!!*

29

AND SOON...

YEHUDAH HAS ORDERED US TO AMBUSH THE TROOPS DOWN THERE. HOW MANY SOLDIERS DO YOU THINK THERE ARE?

WHO KNOWS? THEY KEEP ON COMING AND COMING!

MEANWHILE...

YEHUDAH, THE ENEMY HAS REACHED THE VALLEY.

THAT'S WHAT WE'VE BEEN WAITING FOR!

DEFENDERS, THE TIME HAS COME!!!

ATTACK!!!...

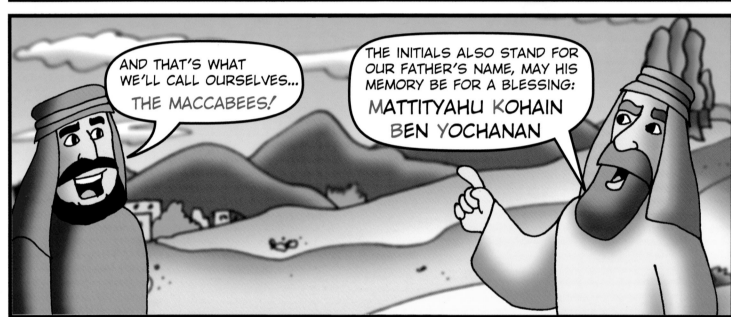

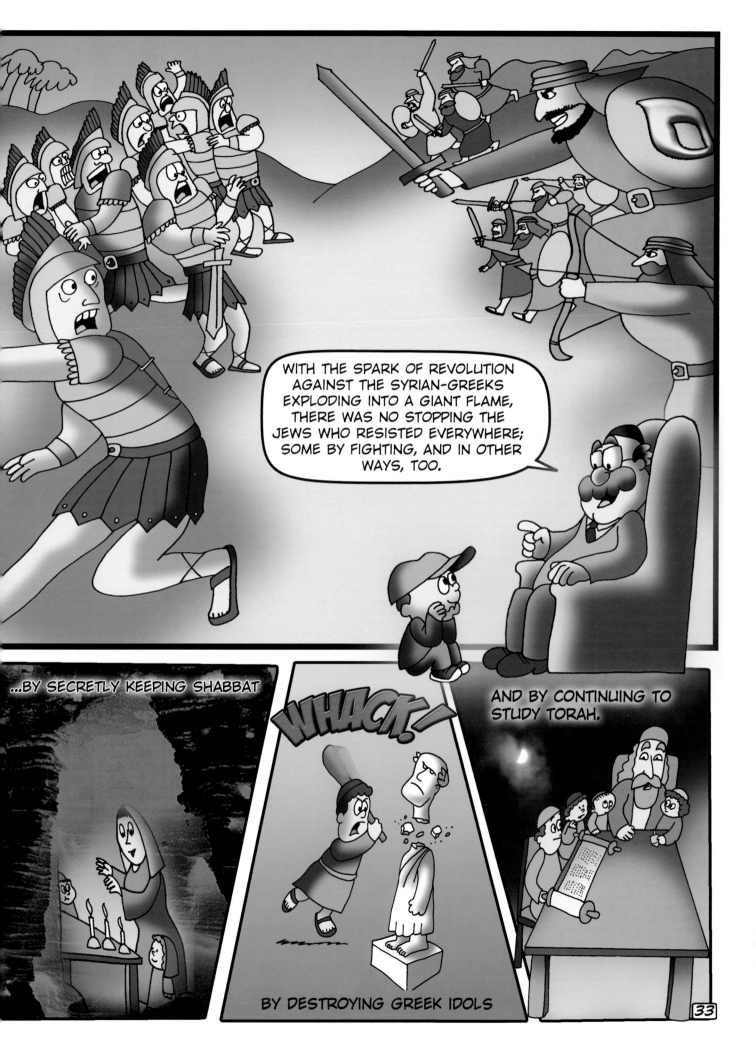

THOUGH HEAVILY OUTNUMBERED, THE MACCABEE FORCES FOUGHT AS THEY'D NEVER FOUGHT BEFORE! AT LAST WHEN THE ECHOES OF BATTLE VANISHED IN THE AIR ABOVE JERUSALEM, THE NEWS SPREAD THROUGHOUT THE LAND; THE HOLY CITY AND THE TEMPLE WERE ONCE AGAIN IN JEWISH HANDS!

SO THE MACCABEES COULD RELAX NOW, ZAIDY?

NOT REALLY BENNY; THE JEWS WOULD FACE MORE YEARS OF HARD FIGHTING TO COMPLETELY FREE THE LAND OF THE GREEKS.
BUT, FOR NOW, THIS WAS AN INCREDIBLE VICTORY!

STILL, THERE WAS A GREAT SHOCK TO COME...

AFTER THE WRECKAGE OF THE WAR WAS CLEARED, THE GRATEFUL PEOPLE GATHERED TO MARCH TOWARD THE HOLY TEMPLE.

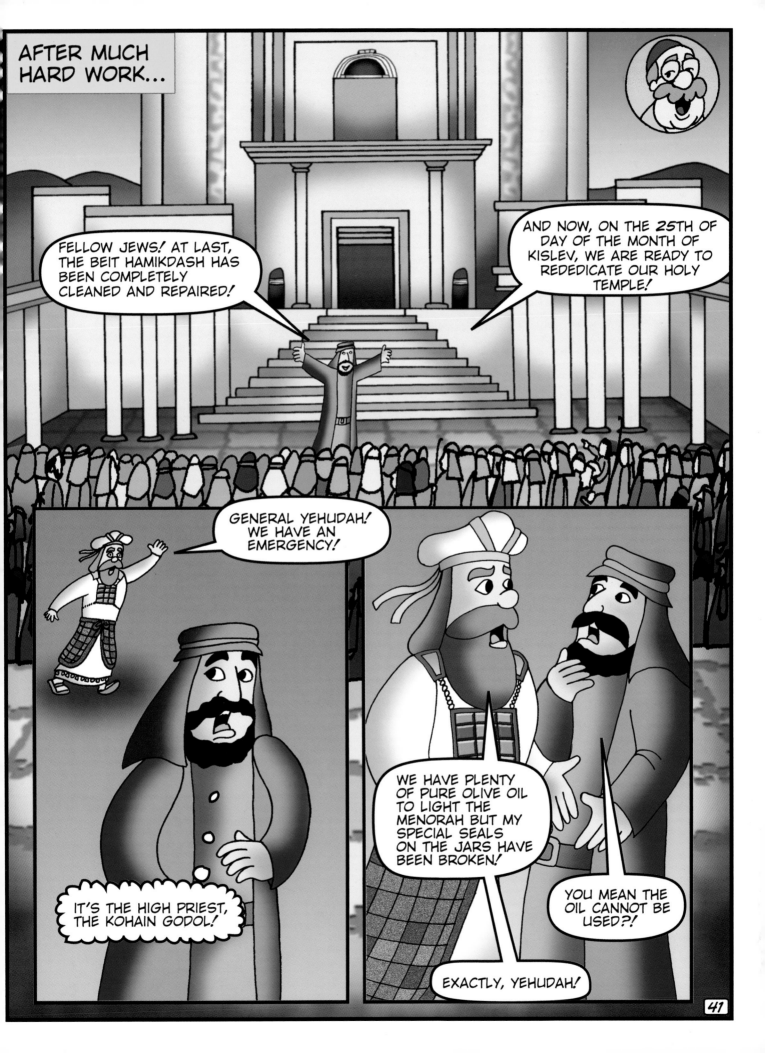

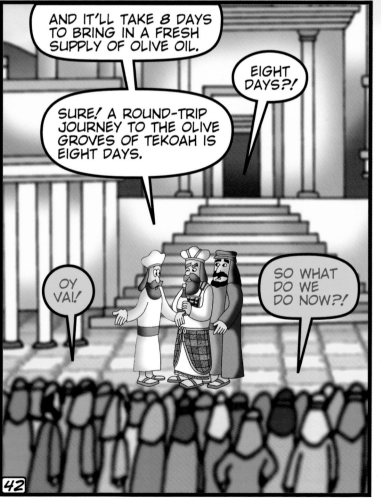

More About Chanukah!

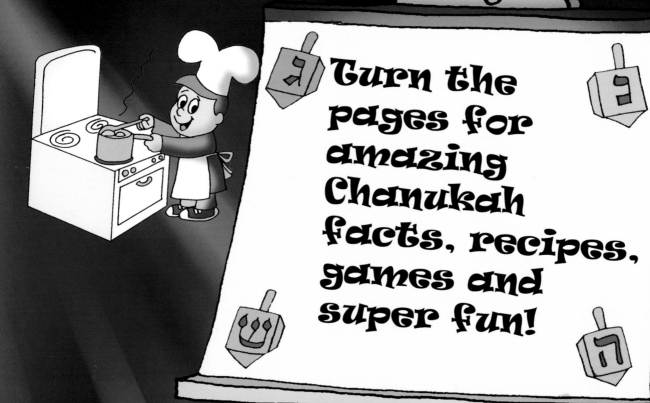

Turn the pages for amazing Chanukah facts, recipes, games and super fun!

And test your knowledge with the QUIZZER!

It's called a slingshot... It worked for King David!

the MOST POPULAR question in JEWISH history!

AND IT'S ABOUT CHANUKAH!

Chanukah is celebrated eight days in honor of the miracle of the oil that lasted eight days. Around 500 years ago, the great scholar, Rabbi Yosef Karo (author of the Shulchan Aruch, the Code of Jewish Law) had this to say on the subject:

"If the jug of oil found in the Beit HaMikdash had enough oil to last one day, why is the first day counted as part of the miracle? Chanukah should be celebrated only 7 days!"

Rabbi Yosef Karo himself gives 3 answers. Throughout the ages, hundreds upon hundreds of additional answers and even entire books have been written to answer this question!

here are a few sample answers:

1. *Winning the war against such a huge, powerful army was a great miracle. To commemorate this, an extra candle is lit.*

2. *The Syrian-Greeks caused all the pure jugs of olive oil to become impure. The finding of one pure jug of oil was also considered a miracle.*

3. *According to an ancient Talmudic manuscript, the jug of oil was not even enough to last one day. So each of the eight days was a miracle!*

The SHAMASH

is the special Menorah candle that lights the other candles. It must be set apart from the others - usually it's higher.

Shamash! That's me! And me!

The caretaker of the synagogue is also called a Shamash. He is the one who opens the shul, puts away the seforim (holy books), sets up for Kiddush, and makes sure that all is in order.

The Shamash is a humble, yet highly important position. Perhaps that's why the Shamash on the menorah is set higher than the other candles.

After all, the Shamash who lit the Menorah in the Beit HaMikdash, was the Kohain Gadol himself!

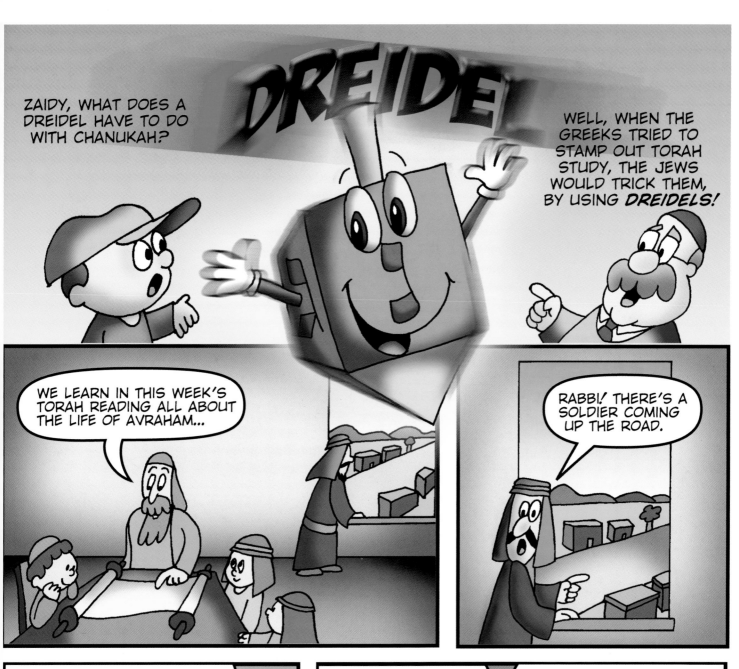

MORE ON... **DREIDEL**

THE WORD "DREIDEL" COMES FROM THE YIDDISH WORD "DREI" MEANING "TURN".

AND ONCE I STOP "DRE-ING", I'LL EXPLAIN THE RULES OF THE DREIDEL GAME.

HOW TO PLAY DREIDEL:

- GIVE EACH PLAYER *15* PENNIES.

- TAKE TURNS SPINNING THE DREIDEL.

- LOOK AT THIS CHART. SEE HOW EACH LETTER ON THE DREIDEL STANDS FOR A YIDDISH WORD AND TEACHES US THE RULES OF THE DREIDEL GAME.

- THE PLAYER WHO ENDS UP WITH ALL THE PENNIES WINS!

IN HEBREW, I'M CALLED A "SVIVON", FROM THE WORD "SAH-VIV", WHICH MEANS "(SPIN) AROUND".

NUN = NISHT (do "nothing")

GIMMEL = GANTZ (take "all" the pennies in the pot - each player then puts in 2 pennies.)

HAY = HALB (take "half" the pennies in the pot.)

SHIN = SHTEL ("put in" 4 pennies in the pot.)

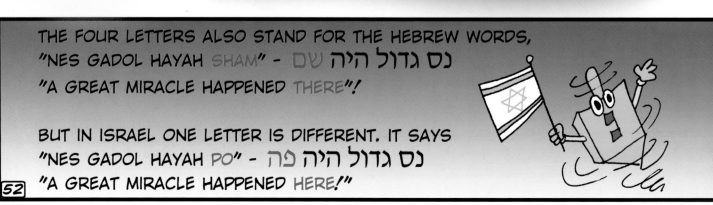

THE FOUR LETTERS ALSO STAND FOR THE HEBREW WORDS, "NES GADOL HAYAH SHAM" - נס גדול היה שם "A GREAT MIRACLE HAPPENED THERE"!

BUT IN ISRAEL ONE LETTER IS DIFFERENT. IT SAYS "NES GADOL HAYAH PO" - נס גדול היה פה "A GREAT MIRACLE HAPPENED HERE!"

Dreidel Ladder Game

EACH PLAYER SHOULD PLACE A MARKER ON THE LADDER.

ALL TOGETHER, WHILE THE PLAYERS SPIN THE DREIDEL, CALL OUT A LETTER – NUN, GIMEL, HAY, OR SHIN.

IF THE DREIDEL STOPS ON THE LETTER OF THE PLAYER'S CHOICE, ADVANCE ONE RUNG ON THE LADDER.

IF IT DOESN'T, STAY WHERE YOU ARE.

NOW GO FOR THE NEXT ROUND.

WINNER

8
7
6
5
4
3
2
1

THE FIRST PLAYER TO REACH THE TOP WINS!

START HERE!

Latkes Recipe

Latkes fried in oil are a favorite Chanukah treat! Remember the miracle of the oil?

Try this simple recipe for some lip-smackin' splendicious latkes!

Here's what you'll need.

2 medium potatoes
1 egg (beaten)
1/4 cup flour
1 teaspoon salt
vegetable oil

Peel and grate the potatoes.

Mix with the beaten egg, flour and salt.

Drop teaspoon size pancakes into hot vegetable oil.

Fry until golden brown on both sides.

Remove latkes from pan and place on paper towel to blot the oil.

Take your pick: Eat it plain or serve with jam, sour cream or apple sauce... YUMMY!

Makes 10-12 small latkes

During the time of Chanukah who ruled the Land of Israel?

So who's ruling the land these days?

Let me check my ruler.

1. Prime Minister Meir Katzenelenbogenstein.

2. Mattityahu Kohain Gadol.

3. King Antiochus.

4. King Latke of Grease.

Where was the main place for JSC (Jewish Service and Celebration)?

1. The JCC (Jerusalem Community Center).

2. The MSH (Maccabee Service Headquarters).

3. The IHOL (International House Of Latkes).

4. The BH (Beit HaMikdash).

Wow... Look at the traffic! Is there a rest area soon?

JSC NEXT EXIT

Why did King Antiochus send his army into Judea?

I WENT TO FIGHT IN JUDEA AND ALL I GOT WAS THIS LOUSY T-SHIRT.

1. To force the Greek culture onto the Jews.

2. To show off his great strength.

3. To teach the Jews how to fight.

4. For a well deserved vacation in the Judean Resort Hills.

What did the Greeks do to get the Jews to assimilate (become like them)?

1. They pretended to be Rabbis.

2. They encouraged the Jews to adopt their way of dress, their language and their sports.

3. They introduced a Dreidel team into the Olympics.

4. They launched a major ad campaign offering a free trip to Greece (hotels included).

What did Antiochus forbid the Jews?

1. Shabbat, Eating Kosher, Learning Torah and Brit Milah.

2. Wearing a Kippah, Tzitzit, Tefillin and Tallit.

3. Wearing a T-Shirt, Pants, Baseball Cap and Shoes (only wreaths, togas and sandals).

4. Eating, Buying, Wearing or Selling any product without a "Made in Greece" sticker.

How were the Jews punished for disobeying Antiochus?

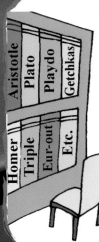

1. They had to write a 1,000 word essay titled, "Why our king is great and lovable."

2. Death.

3. 40 lashes (ouch!).

4. Being forced to drink eight cups of olive oil (ugh!!)

Looks Greek to me!

What did the Greeks do to the holy books and Torah scrolls?

You're holding it upside down... Klutz!

1. Translated them into Greek.

2. Recycled them to be used for Greek books.

3. Burned them.

4. Sold them to the highest bidder.

What terrible things did the Greeks do in the Holy Temple (besides wrecking it)?

1. They converted it into an indoor sports arena.

2. They brought in idols and sacrificed a pig.

3. They brought in idols and sacrificed an elephant.

4. They wrote graffiti on all the giant pillars.

Quite a place they got here!

Yeah, let's redecorate... Greek style

You ready to fight Antiochus' army?

Sure, as soon as I figure out how to plug this thing in.

Who led the Jewish resistance?

1. Yehuda Dreidle, a very wealthy Jew.

2. Chana and her seven sons.

3. Mattityahu and his five sons.

4. An Italian Jew named Bertolli - owner of the famous Bertolli Oil Company.

Which of the following was NOT one of Mattityahu's sons?

Huh?

1. **Elazar**

2. Yonatan.

3. Yehuda.

4. Yisroel.

He followed us home, father. Can we keep him? He'll bite the enemy soldiers.

What was the strategy of the small Jewish army in fighting the massive Greek army?

1. They used LATKES
Laser Automatic Timed Killer Explosive Systems.

2. They ambushed them in surprise attacks.

3. Each arrow they shot miraculously turned into hundreds!

4. Absolutely no strategy... they just went ahead to fight!

It's called a slingshot... It worked for King David!

After Mattityahu died...

1. ...the Jewish revolt died with him.

2. ...his son Yehuda and his four brothers continued to lead the Jewish army.

3. The Greeks easily defeated the Jewish troops.

4. The Jews ate latkes on his Yahrtzeit (anniversary of his death).

MIRACLE LIGHTS QUIZZER

What was the battle cry of the Jewish fighters'?

> Two, four, six, eight
> The Syrian-Greeks are not so great!

1. Mi Kamocha Ba'eilim HaShem - Who is strong like You, HaShem?

2. Nes Gadol Haya Po - A great miracle happened here!

3. Greece Greet Green Geese (Try saying that ten times fast!) .

4. Hit them with a Hammer (Maccabee)! Put 'em in the Slammer!

At last the Maccabees succeeded in capturing...

> Hey, look! I captured this enemy soldier!

> That's a lion!

> No, it's the truth!

1. ...Antiochus, the wicked king.

2. ... pictures of the Greek Army on their new digital cameras.

3. ... an entire year's supply of fresh latkes.

4. ...Jerusalem and the Beit HaMikdash.

When Jerusalem was back in Jewish hands, the Maccabees faced...

1. ...the task of repairing the wrecked Temple.

2. ...the decision whether to make Yehudah the king.

3. ...the problem of who'll cater the victory party.

4. ...the difficulty of breaking the news to Antiochus.

> Whew... thank goodness the fighting's over!

> Uh, dear, this mail just came in for you from headquarters.

THINGS TO DO AFTER BATTLE

1.
2.
3.
4.
5.
6.
7.
8.

When the Holy Temple was finally repaired, the Jews were shocked to see...

Hooray! The Temple is finally repaired!

Great! So you can finally fix the basement leak?

1. ... the huge cleaning bill.

2. ... a big box of musical dreidels.

3. ... all the jugs of oil with broken seals.

4. ... all the mezuzahs were stolen.

Who helped with the cleaning of the Bait HaMikdash?

1. The Maccabees.

2. Alex's Cleaning Crew Inc.

3. Antiochus and two of his generals.

4. Plenty of Jewish volunteers.

Holy City Cleaners? Can you get graffiti off of pillars?

No... Not pillows... PILLARS!

Why is Chanukah celebrated for eight days?

I know! For eight days we get no homework! Right?

1. ...That's how long the oil of the Menorah miraculously burned.

Nice try, Benny.

2. ...Wonder of wonders! It took only eight days to clean and repair the Temple!

3. ...The Rabbis decided that Jewish kids needed a long winter holiday.

4. ...Since all Chanukah Menorahs have eight candles.

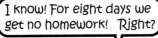

Why do we eat latkes fried in oil on Chanukah?

1. Ever try frying latkes in pickle juice?

2. That was the main food of the Macabbees while fighting in the hills of Judea.

3. To remind us of the miracle of the oil.

4. Because they taste so delicious!

In Israel, what do the letters on the dreidel stand for?

I can't think... I'm too dizzy!

1. Support Israel... Buy Israel bonds.

2. A great miracle happened here.

3. A great miracle happened there.

4. Made from recycled materials.

What is not considered one of the miracles of Chanukah?

1. Winning a war against the powerful army.

2. Finding one pure jug of oil after the Temple had been wrecked.

3. The Beit HaMikdash was repaired in just eight days.

4. The oil lasted for eight days.

It's a miracle!

What happened?

I didn't burn the latkes!

What is written on the dreidel?

1. Nes Gadol Haya Sham.

2. Made in China.

3. Ad Kan Hakofo Alef.

4. Oil, Potatoes, Onions, Garlic.

So what is written on the dreidel?

I can't tell; It's spinning too fast!

What are Sufganiyot?

Take two sufganiyot and call me in the morning.

KISLEV 25

DR. FALAFFEL

1. What the Greeks called the Maccabees.

2. Doughnuts filled with jelly.

3. A Mideastern remedy for a headache, sore throat and the common cold.

4. The Hebrew word for "dreidels."

What happened on the 25th of Kislev?

1. The Jews rested from the war.

2. The battle for Jerusalem was won.

3. The first annual Dreidel contest was won.

4. "Miracle Lights" was finally printed.

Oops... I don't think the answer is here.